I
am
Worthy

Desiree Mangandog, L.Ac

© 2018 by Desiree Mangandog

ISBN 978-1-732059-3-7

Edited by Genevieve Kim

Cover and Interior Book Design by Rachel Gayle

Printed and bound in the United States of America
Kase Printing, Hudson, NH www.kaseprinting.com
First Printing September 2018

Published by Rhythm & Flow Project, LLC.
Spanaway, Washington 98387

Visit www.desireemangandog.com

To the ones who have been marginalized and called crazy...

you are worthy.

Contents

Foreword

*C*reating a steady, capable container for energy is the primary intent of any nourishing practice. Whether it's meditation, yoga, acupuncture, or the consistent use of Essential Oils, for the past twenty years this aim has fueled my choices - both for my choice of profession and my own self-care.

Encountering Desiree's work was for me a delicious moment of worlds colliding. With that same intent to stabilize and harmonize the body and mind, in our first meeting I felt my years of receiving acupuncture treatments and my love of the Oils merging, and everything shifted. Her work has made my life lighter, freer and more satisfying.

While Desiree's extensive experiential understanding of Chinese Medicine fuels the wisdoms she shares, it's her acceptance of her own intuitive gifts that allows her to bring the resonance of Essential Oils into an even higher realm of efficacy. Working with her teaches me to see and treat myself as I would a sacred friend; in her first book I continue to find myself and my heart again and again. With every application and each blend she suggests, I move closer to new levels of listening and thankfulness.

The book you hold in your hands is a masterful

reminder of your truth, your worthiness and your wholeness. The details provided herein offer you a map to help you clear what's blocking you, nurture the patterns that empower you, and harmonize your new understanding of your most subtle strengths. I dare you to follow Desiree's lead and experience a fresh, evolved story of yourself, a tale of exquisite embodiment, fluent flow and steady harmony within and around you.

Elena Brower,

Author of PRACTICE YOU
and ART OF ATTENTION

New York

Introduction

Introduction

My dear soul friend,

Thank you for your vulnerability and trusting in me to guide you. It is an honor to build this intimate relationship with you. As you read these words and implement the protocols from this book, know that I can feel it. I feel your sorrow, and I feel your joy, and I certainly feel your love.

The purpose of this book is to help you release the wounds you carry in your heart, to free your spirit, and to live the greatest expression of yourself. Prepare to experience massive transitions, a new outlook, and more desired outcomes to appear. All I ask is for you to play full out with me. If you follow the steps and participate in the exercises, I guarantee transformation will happen. And when you have completed the work, please share with me your experiences.

I look forward to getting to know you and meeting you face to face one day.

Cheers to living life by your design.

With love,

Desiree

IF THIS IS OUR *first* ENCOUNTER ...

It is a pleasure to meet you.

My name is Desiree Mangandog. Before I list out all the fancy titles by my name, I'd love to share with you my spirit. This way, you can decide if the work in this book resonates with you.

I am a warrior. I have come to this world to create a revolution of healing. It pains my heart to see individuals beat themselves up as a "worthless nobody," when I see the greatness within them and the problems they are destined to solve with their talents. My obsession is to find tools and techniques that will free oneself from limiting beliefs and trapped emotions that hinder their progress. Once these have been released, the possibilities are limitless. With a love for plants and energy medicine, I have found a way to use essential oils to shift energy in the body, mind, and spirit.

My background is in Chinese Medicine. I am a licensed Acupuncturist and Herbalist. There are many philosophies and styles in the world of Chinese Medicine, including Traditional Chinese Medicine, Japanese Style, Korean Hand Acupuncture, Eight Principles, Five Elements, etc. It was quite tumultuous going through school trying to figure out which "style" of acupuncture was right for me. After a few years of navigating all the different methods, though, I finally found one that captured my heart.

It is called Classical Five Elements acupuncture. The core philosophy of this discipline is:

99% of illnesses are rooted in the spirit, and only 1% is physical.

I didn't fully understand this concept until a few years ago. It was in July 2015 when all that I had learned in my early 20's and years of private practice came together into a complete picture. Don't you love when that happens? You reflect back on something you were told 10 or 15 years ago, didn't get it at the time, but then randomly it all makes sense now?

So what happened July 2015?

My husband and I went to a Tony Robbins event called UNLEASH THE POWER WITHIN. (If you haven't been, I highly recommend!) There was a three-hour guided visualization called the "Dickens Process", which helps to associate pain with not doing something. The audience is guided through a scene in Charles Dickens' A CHRISTMAS CAROL when the main character, Ebenezer Scrooge, meets the *Ghost of Christmas Future* and shows what the future would be like if he continues his current behavior and choices.

This meditation did so much more than associate pain with not completing a project. Right after that meditation, I went through a type of spiritual awakening I had never experienced. A great analogy to describe my experience would be how Neo in THE MATRIX was catapulted into a new reality almost instantly. After Neo swallows the red pill, he wakes up from an existence he thought was real but was in fact an illusion, and is instead ejected into a new reality where he sees for the first time the harsh realities of the human race.

I, too, woke up to a new reality. I began to see the meridians and chakras in people. I could hear, taste, smell, feel and see their emotions. The spirit realms of angels and demons came to life. It was incredible and scary at the same time. For three months, I could not be around people. I could hear their judgments and taste their emotions. It became overwhelming. After three months of suffering, I finally prayed to God for help. (By the way, I use the term God when referring to creator, universe, life, spirit.) This level of sensitivity, though at first seemed like a curse, was in fact a blessing. With these sensitivities I was able to hear God's inspiration and create powerful blends and protocols to heal others. I kept hearing that I needed to share these tools with anyone who was willing to listen. At the time, the pain of rejection was excruciating, but I held on to the faithful words that God voiced to me: "I promise this is temporary". After months of putting myself out there, and people looking at me like I had lost my mind, people finally started to listen.

Now I sit before you, writing my second book three years later, still grateful for those blessings and still fully devoted to sharing the work that I was asked to teach. If you're willing to listen, keep reading.

WELCOME

Welcome to I AM WORTHY! I am bursting with excitement as I share this profound work with you. It is a dream of mine that all persons own their divine worth so they may soar in this life. It is imperative that you thrive and accomplish all your dreams because it heals the rest of humanity. *Never* underestimate how valuable you are. Your daily interactions and activities create a ripple effect of either expansion or contraction in the collective consciousness. The entire premise of this book is that **you matter.** (Yes, read that again.)

You don't matter just a little, You matter A LOT.

You have the power to influence another person's life in a significant way, just as I have with others.

I honor you for being brave and doing work that may be unfamiliar, sound a little strange, and at times feel utterly painful. By the time you have worked through each of the chapters, you can expect to experience a resolve in you that you haven't felt before:

inner-strength, peace and a drive to accomplish your soul work. Call me selfish, but I want to experience your art! I love being inspired and uplifted by individuals who are living in the flow and fully expressing their authentic self.

Your Genius, UNLOCKS MY GENIUS, AND my Genius, UNLOCKS YOURS.

-Desiree Mangandog

COMMITTING TO THE PROCESS

The best results happen by doing the work, and I am committed to your success. Are you? If so, please read and sign your commitment below.

I, _Carrie Morgan Ford_ commit to applying the protocols, blends, and exercises that are outlined in "I am Worthy". If I miss a day, then I will pick up where I left off the next day.

Feeling Emotions:

As I use the recommended essential oils, I understand that repressed emotions and memories may surface. This can lead to experiencing uncomfortable emotions such as despair, fear, sadness, rage, and grief. I understand that this is part of the healing process, and I commit to loving myself with compassion and kindness during this time of healing. I must feel and move through stagnant emotions in order to be free of them. After an application, I may experience crying spells or rage spells for a few minutes. (This can happen within 24 hours of a protocol.)

Once I have completed a release, I will allow myself to feel lightness, whether it be physical and/or emotional.

To help with detoxing trapped emotions, I commit to taking care of myself and will:

1. Drink more water than usual as I move through the weeks.

2. Take epsom salt baths on the days I am struggling. (Maybe even float in a sensory deprivation tank!)

3. Exercise however I feel my body needs, whether

it's cardio, weight lifting, HIIT, yoga, pilates, martial arts, qi gong, etc.

4. Journal Writing. Even if I don't have a practice of doing so, I will commit to writing while going through "I Am Worthy", as I know it will help with processing emotions as well as documenting and celebrating my progress. (Writing is extremely cathartic. For some, there are releases that only the act of writing can do.)

5. Use essential oils, whether they are the ones outlined in this book or the ones I feel my body is craving. I will honor the energy of the oils as my body needs.

6. Meditate. When difficult feelings come to the surface, I will allow myself the space to sit with them. Breathe through them. I will allow these feelings and thoughts to pass.

7. Tapping. This can be EFT or just simply taking the tips of my fingers and tapping anywhere on my body that I feel the tension, such as tapping on my heart and chest when I feel anxious. (For more information about tapping, see the Resources page.)

I, _Carrie Morgan Ford_, am fully committed because *I am Worthy*.

Signature _Carrie Ford_

Date _9-25-18_

TOOLS FOR HEALING

Here is a list of the essential oils needed for this book. If you do not have essential oils, you can go to my website at *www.desireemangandog.com* to purchase the highest quality and most effective essential oils.

≋ESSENTIAL OILS *list* ≋

- ☐ Basil
- ☐ Bergamot
- ☐ Black Pepper
- ☐ Cardamom
- ☐ Cassia
- ☐ Cedarwood
- ☐ Clary Sage
- ☐ Copaiba
- ☐ Coriander
- ☐ Cypress
- ☐ Douglas Fir
- ☐ Eucalyptus
- ☐ Frankincense

- ☐ Geranium
- ☐ Ginger
- ☐ Grapefruit
- ☐ Helichrysum
- ☐ Indian Sandalwood
- ☐ Juniper Berry
- ☐ Lavender
- ☐ Lemon
- ☐ Lemongrass
- ☐ Lime
- ☐ Melaleuca
- ☐ Myrrh

- ☐ Neroli
- ☐ Patchouli
- ☐ Peppermint
- ☐ Petitgrain
- ☐ Roman Chamomile
- ☐ Rosemary
- ☐ Siberian Fir
- ☐ Tangerine
- ☐ Vetiver
- ☐ Wild Orange
- ☐ Wintergreen
- ☐ Ylang Ylang

Optional: ☐ Grounding Blend

THE PROCESS

There are many techniques used to create change in the body, mind, and spirit. Essential oils are one of my favorite tools to cause profound energetic shifts.

The Science Behind the Oils

Quantum physics teaches us that we are made of waves of energy. Our cells are made up of molecules, which are then made up of atoms. An atom is an invisible force field that emits waves of electrical energy. When you break down an atom, 99.999999999999% of the atom is waves of energy. Only .000000000001% is physical matter - particles of electrons, protons, and neutrons. Hence, your body is mostly energy.

The frequency of energy you experience affects how your cells function. So what moves all this energy within our system? Our emotions. I first heard Tony Robbins brilliantly say this:

emotions = ENERGY in motion

There are emotions that have lower frequencies that lead to disease, and emotions with higher frequencies that create a healthy movement of energy within the body.

In Chinese Medicine (CM), our main objective is to create a smooth flow of qi (energy) in all the organs and meridians. It is the stagnation of qi that causes disease. To give an example, what happens in a stagnant pool of water like a swamp? Disease-ridden mosquitos, poisonous snakes, leeches, unpleasant odors, etc.

We use the term "stress" too loosely in our culture to indicate a variety of emotional experiences. However, "stress" is an indication of the physiological flight or fight response in our body. This means that when we are stressed, we are operating in emergency mode and are only concerned with our survival. Stress will produce lower frequencies that cause cells to function below their optimal capabilities. Our thoughts affect the emotions we experience, and emotions directly affect our physical health.

In this book, we will tackle the lowest frequency of emotions that most people carry. It is the frequency of worthlessness and shame. In that same frequency is also blame, as blame is one way shame is expressed.

I have found that when a person understands their divine worth and completely accepts who they are that person experiences a profound level of peace and freedom that the soul truly desires. This is where I have found the power of essential oils to come into play. By using essential oils on very specific acupuncture points and meridians, the body is able to transform the lower frequencies stored in our cells to elevated frequencies, and infuse the body with a new vibration that empowers the individual to live their highest expression.

The Sequence of Using the Oils

As a practitioner of Chinese Medicine, I have a specific sequence in moving stagnant energy. It is done with intention and precision. It is not enough to clear out an obstruction. Smooth, harmonious flow must follow. This is the art and ancient wisdom of Chinese Medicine that I fell in love with. The protocols

I have created combine the sequencing and energetic points of Chinese Medicine with the healing vibrations of essential oils together. Much observation, love, and intention have been put into this work to ensure your safe progress.

Step 1: Clear Stagnation

The first step is to clear the insult or obstruction. In this case, we are releasing trapped emotions and limiting beliefs surrounding worthlessness. When a pattern is stubborn, though, I may use essential oils to loosen the grip before it gets cleared away. Some stories are deep, so in these instances I will add an additional step of preparation before clearing. (Preparation when stories are deep is critical, as we do not want to shock the body with too much radical change at once.)

Step 2: Nourish

The second step is to integrate a new pattern that is empowering and desired. It isn't enough to clear. When you clear *I'm not good enough* and fail to introduce *I'm more than enough*, a vacuum of energy can occur and may manifest into a mental/emotional breakdown. In these situations an identity crisis may arise. The body and spirit is resilient and can correct itself, but the withdrawals and detox symptoms may be long and harsh if this second step of nourishment is ignored.

Step 3: Harmonize

The third step is to harmonize the new frequencies throughout the body. Introducing a new pattern, such as *I'm more than enough*, can be a dramatic change and foreign to a person's spirit. In order to prevent the body/mind/spirit from rejecting *I'm more than enough* harmonizing is an important step to move through this transition.

An example I often share in my workshops is organ transplants. When a person receives a new organ transplant, medication may be given to prevent the body from rejecting the new organ. Ideally, the patient wants the body to recognize the new organ as its own. The harmonizing of Step 3, like the medication, helps the body to recognize and receive the new organ. Frankincense is one of the greatest harmonizing essential oils. I use it often to integrate and lock in a new pattern so that the new pattern becomes the new normal.

Throughout our time together in this book, we will be alternating between weeks of clearing with nourishing and harmonizing. Here is the schedule for the next five weeks. It will be outlined in each chapter as well.

Chapter 1: Week 1 (Days 1-7)

Chapter 2: Week 2 (Days 8-14)

Chapter 3: Week 3 (Days 15-17)

Chapter 4: Week 3 (Days 18-21)

Chapter 5: Week 4 (Days 22-28)

Chapter 6: Week 5 (Days 29-35)

Though I'm a huge fan of getting the quickest results, we must also be safe, sustainable and gradual as well. Please do not rush through the process. If you miss a day, pick up where you left off. Trust the process. Be patient and stay consistent. I am here to guide you step by step.

You are perfectly whole and complete. The question is, do you believe it? Do you own it? Do you embody this truth?

WHY WORTHINESS?

Self-worth is a deep understanding that *I matter.*

You matter completely. You are important. Your thoughts, feelings, desires, vision, voice, and spirit matter. This sense is deeply rooted within our soul. Your worth is not dependent upon outside praise, others' opinions, achievements, accomplishments, circumstances, what you do or do not do, what you have or don't have. You already have everything you need inside of you.

Self-worth is deeper than self-confidence. In essence, it is about knowing your divine nature and the beauty that exists in your soul.

Without a strong sense of self-worth, doubts and fears may easily fill our spirit. This leads to a blockage in fulfilling the vision and mission that is our life's purpose. It is our growth, evolution, contribution, and emotional maturity that catapult healing.

Self-worth is this underlying frequency that colors every aspect of our being. How we interact with others, the content of our conversations, access to our creativity, productivity and efficiency in our work, the ability to feel and receive love from the Divine, how we parent our children, and most importantly, our internal peace.

Disease is predicated on a lack of flow and harmony. The primary focus of a Chinese Medical practitioner is to create flow and harmony within the organs and meridians. Unworthiness entangles through the meridians and chakras, creating stagnation all throughout body systems. A key principle in achieving health in Chinese Medicine is:

"When there is free flow, there is no pain. When there is no free flow, there is pain."

By increasing your self-worth, you are practicing unconditional love towards yourself. Which then leads to an outpouring of unconditional love towards others. I know you are reading this book because you want to uplift yourself and others.

However, without a strong sense of self-worth, we become a drain on society rather than a contributor. That may sound harsh, but if we are depleted, how can we uplift others? Ask yourself: are you generating more love for yourself and others, or are you depleting vitality? Take a moment to observe without judgment the way of your patterns. No need for shame, just observation.

ENERGY FREQUENCY

Let's take a look at this chart from David Hawkin's book, POWER VS. FORCE:

Map of Consciousness
DEVELOPED BY DAVID R. HAWKINS

Name of Level	Energetic Frequency	Emotional State	View of Life
ENLIGHTENMENT	700-1000	INEFFABLE	IS
PEACE	600	BLISS	PERFECT
JOY	540	SERENITY	COMPLETE
LOVE	500	REVERANCE	BENIGN
REASON	400	UNDERSTANDING	MEANINGFUL
ACCEPTANCE	350	FORGIVENESS	HARMONIOUS
WILLINGNESS	310	OPTIMISM	HOPEFUL
NEUTRALITY	250	TRUST	SATISFACTORY
COURAGE	200	AFFIRMATION	FEASIBLE
PRIDE	175	SCORN	DEMANDING
ANGER	150	HATE	ANTAGONISTIC
DESIRE	125	CRAVING	DISSAPPOINTING
FEAR	100	ANXIETY	FRIGHTENING
GRIEF	75	REGRET	TRAGIC
APATHY	50	DESPAIR	HOPELESS
GUILT	30	BLAME	EVIL
SHAME	20	HUMILIATION	MISERABLE

POWER / FORCE

SHAME = WORTHLESSNESS

You will notice that shame is at the very bottom of emotional frequencies. It is the slowest of frequencies that creates the most stagnation in the body, mind, and spirit. Shame is the ultimate contracted state of being that prohibits health and vitality. This is also the frequency that allows disease-causing organisms to thrive, such as viruses, harmful bacteria, candida, parasites, etc.

To summarize, unworthiness is a diseased state. This is not a truthful depiction of who we are as humans. Scientists have calculated that the odds of you being born are one in 400 trillion! What a miracle you are! You are created with extreme intention, not randomness. You are of high worth, and we all need you. We want to experience your love, your art, your creations to improve the conditions of this world.

The more you clear your lower frequencies, the more you up-level your life experiences. Unworthiness breeds scarcity: feelings of "not enough," anxiety, comparison, judgement, jealousy, and blame. The part of unworthiness that bothers me the most in people is how it squashes our ability to see other possibilities. It creates the illusion of being trapped, causes hopelessness, and limits perspective to envision something new for ourselves. It almost feels like your body and spirit are treading through the mud. Clogged.

The good news is there is a way out! We will be applying essential oils, diffusing them, and including a few exercises to help you break through the gunk of unworthiness.

Before we dive into the work, understand that as humans we are complex in nature and have multiple layers of experiences and emotions. I encourage you to move through the chapters in this book sequentially. However, understand that this is a process and that we are breaking years and years of patterns, and that takes time. Rest assured though, you will experience a huge weight off your shoulders and notice marked improvement in your inner well-being and the reality you create.

There are memories and emotions you are ready to release at this time. And there may be another round of memories and emotions you are ready to release six months from now. Honor the timing of your healing. The oils and protocols will take care of the most pressing issues in this current moment. I encourage you to keep revising the entire process outlined in this book. Like a snake sheds its skin, so, too, do we shed patterns, and this process will help you move through that sacred transition.

Once again, I would like to thank you for taking this bold move by doing the work.

As you heal yourself, others heal.

We are one human community, and what we focus on affects the whole. Your wellness affects my wellness. And my wellness affects yours.

So let's get moving!

Chapter 1: Clear the Noise

Energy Exchanges

very day, every moment, we are constantly exchanging energy from our environment and interactions. There are exchanges that uplift us and provide great movement to our energy body, and there are exchanges that deplete our vitality. Hence why it is important that we carefully choose those we surround ourselves with, the places we go, the media we consume, and the activities in which we partake. This point is not to make you paranoid, but rather to remind you to become mindful of your daily interactions and to check in with your intuition to make better decisions.

It is especially critical in our modern-day lifestyle. For most of our human history, we have not experienced the amount of information and opinions we are bombarded with today. It's quite daunting the amount of ads we consume, the updates on over 500 friends through social media, the amount of correspondences (texts, email, phone calls, messages), the entertainment we listen to and watch. I remember times when it was exciting to receive a letter in the mail from one person! And now getting 50 emails in a day is normal.

Opportunities for silence, reflection, and listening to our inner voice have decreased as more opportunities for clicks, scrolls, likes, texts, etc. have increased.

And we need those critical moments of pause and silence to connect to our inspiration, healing, and divine communication.

As we interact with the world, noise and unwanted energies can get stuck in our auric field. Grimy, sticky energy can cloud the field and affect healthy flow in our systems. So the first thing we are going to do is clear the noise out of your auric field.

WHAT IS THE AURIC FIELD?

The auric field is an energy field that surrounds your body and is an extension of you. Within this field, information is stored regarding your condition. This field also contains Wei Qi (Defensive Qi), which protects the body from outside pathogens. It is critical to keep the auric field clean and strong so that there is a direct path for inspiration and divine messages to flow.

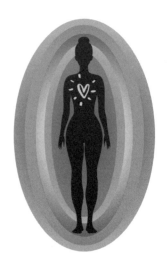

WHAT IS NOISE?

Noise is another way of describing the unwanted energies that are contributing to disease.

The dictionary defines noise as a sound, especially one that is loud or unpleasant or that causes a disturbance.

"Noise," according to MERRIAM-WEBSTER DICTIONARY:

1. Loud, confused, senseless shouting or outcry

2. Any sound that is undesired or interferes with one's hearing of something

I consider noise to be any idea, thought, energy, or emotion that does not belong to you and does not resonate with the true nature of your soul. A question to ask yourself is, *Am I exposing myself and taking in what is right and healthy for me?* This is not about absolute right and wrong, as one person's medicine may be another's allergy. This also applies to people, media, food, music and other sources of information. Choose what feeds your soul and discard that which does not serve you.

In this chapter, we will focus on external noise and address internal noise in another chapter. External noise influences our inner self-talk that can be shaming and discouraging, and by clearing external noise, we quiet the incessant inner critic.

THE IMPORTANCE OF CLEARING THE NOISE

Imagine you have just inherited a fixer-upper home. There is so much potential, but there is also a great deal of restoration required before moving into it. Years of neglect have led to serious mold build-up, termite damage, and rodent infestation. Before any remodeling begins, clearing the space of these damages is the first task. If the toxic waste is not removed, further damage will ensue -- mold will continue to spread and termites will strip away the core of the building. We must address the noise first, so we can begin deep work and restore the spirit in wholeness.

Every thought or feeling we have about someone else always has an effect. That thought or feeling does not remain confined to you. Instead, it emanates outside of your body and travels to the person of your thoughts. This is why prayer is so powerful. If feelings of jealousy arise towards a friend, though, that energy will travel across space and time and reach her. She may or may not consciously pick up on this energy, depending on her levels of sensitivity. If hypersensitive, she will experience feelings of betrayal, heartache, or loneliness at the same time I am having negative thoughts about her. If her boundaries are strong, though, she will not experience the vibration of negativity; only I would bear the unpleasant feeling of jealousy and experience emptiness. Attacking another person is no different from attacking ourselves, as we are one.

We as a human community are highly connected.

Even if words are unspoken, the energies and feelings are felt. This is why I regularly practice taking inventory of my mental and emotional experiences, observing what destructive emotions may be coming my way, or the ones I am sending to another person. It is a continual practice. By no means can most of us reach this perfect level of enlightenment. All we can do is improve. The goal is to reach a level of respect and unconditional love toward all persons, no matter what they say or do.

EXAMPLES OF NOISE

Here are examples of noisy, gunky energies that can get trapped in your auric field:

- Negative opinions and judgements (spoken or unspoken) from people

- Disempowering thoughts and emotions of the people around you

- Media, including movies, shows, documentaries, videos and interviews, that create more fear and anxiety

- Physical environments that drain your energy

- Excessive scrolling through social media platforms

- Advertisements that create an excessive focus on the material world, and set up standards that are far from the truth. (i.e., how women must be stick thin to be considered beautiful)

- **Problems and burdens of others and the world. Specifically when the majority of the focus is on the problem without a focus on the solution.**

Our environment deeply affects our worldview, moods, and behaviors. When we surround ourselves with family members, friends, co-workers, and acquaintances who operate under a paradigm of scarcity, over time we may adopt those same frequencies.

People with a "filthy" auric field tend to lack self-confidence and are easily influenced by the opinions of others. They also lack clarity, which is a key component to affecting others in a positive way. A noisy field breeds confusion, mood swings, depression, fear, anxiousness, and irritability. But, as you learn how to "clear the noise" and build healthy boundaries, your environment will have less of an impact on you, and your clean and strong auric field will have more of an influence on others.

A side note for my hypersensitive friends who are empaths and intuitive:

This chapter will completely change how you operate in this world. (Hypersensitives consist of approximately 10% of the population.) Because you have the ability to sense what is going on emotionally with people being in public may be a challenge as you can pick up on multiple peoples' emotions simultaneously. Feelings of overwhelming anxiety may cause you to want to retreat to a quiet place. Confusion can set in as you struggle to differentiate your own emotions versus other people's emotions. Over time collecting so many people's emotional baggage can weigh you down and dampen your intuitive gifts.

Simple essential oils, however, can completely change how you function around people with grace and ease. If you keep your auric field clear of other peoples' energies, you will be free. After connecting with someone, you will have the power to clear any residual energy that no longer serves you by using the protocols outlined in this chapter.

WEEK 1 PROTOCOL: *Clear the Noise*

Please note: there are three parts to this protocol, and each one is essential. Complete each part. Afterall, you are **worthy** *of it all.*

WRITING OUT YOUR THOUGHTS

Find a comfortable place to relax. Take some time to sit there and begin to unwind. Why write?

Document your life, my friend, because ♥ your life matters. ♥

Writing is a powerful healing tool. A release happens as the words leave your mind and land on paper. Destructive thoughts swirling around your head and stagnant energies in your heart compound over time. They need an outlet. Those thoughts and stagnant energies literally drain through your arm and out the fingertips, leaving your spirit for good. Also, handwriting is more effective than typing. In acupuncture, the practitioner uses the fine point of a needle to concentrate healing energy into the acupuncture point. Like a needle, the pen on paper is doing the same.

- What are some disempowering thoughts that consume my attention lately?

- What does my inner critic say about my current life circumstances?

- What do I complain about the most?

- What are the thoughts that are making me feel bad about myself and life in general?

Write down what initially comes to mind, including the thoughts that are negatively impacting your mood and behaviors. There is no wrong way to do this. Here are some examples to give you an idea...

I'm not doing enough as a parent.
I feel inadequate at my workplace
I am overwhelmed with my to-do-list
Too much to do, so little time
I don't know what I'm doing with my life
Why am I so lazy?
Why can't I break this habit?
I am frustrated with everyone around me
People are always taking advantage of my kindness
I don't know what I'm doing
People stress me out
Nobody notices me
Life is not fun
Life is too hard
I'm tired

Write your top five disempowering thoughts below. Next to each one, provide a numeric value to indicate the level of intensity felt for each one.

0 - *Thought does not affect me*
5 - *Thought has somewhat of a negative impact*
10 - *Thought has a crippling impact*

1. _____

_____ *Level of Intensity:* _____

2. _____

_____ *Level of Intensity:* _____

3. _____

_____ *Level of Intensity:* _____

4. _____

_____ *Level of Intensity:* _____

5. _____

_____ *Level of Intensity:* _____

You did it! How often do you purge that way? May this exercise show you the power of writing and its healing capabilities.

For the next seven days, we will pair an essential oil blend, a protocol, and a diffuser blend to further clear the noises you wrote down. Each day of application will chip away at the intensity of those annoying thoughts/emotions.

Clear the Noise

USE DURING WEEK 1: DAYS 1-7

TOOLS:

☐ 10mL Roller Bottle   ☐ Fractionated Coconut Oil

ESSENTIAL OILS:

☐ Melaleuca   ☐ Wintergreen   ☐ Cypress
☐ Lemongrass   ☐ Cedarwood

PREPARATION:

Add (8) drops Melaleuca, (3) drops Wintergreen, (3) drops Cypress, (3) drops Lemongrass, and (3) drops Cedarwood into the 10mL roller bottle. Fill the rest of the roller bottle to the top with Fractionated Coconut Oil.

APPLICATION:

Roll the blend on the back of the neck, the midline of the belly, and on the inside of the elbow creases. Apply two times per day in the morning and in the late afternoon.

Clear the Noise Blend Breakdown

Melaleuca is the chief essential oil in this blend. If you look at Melaleuca's physical properties, it is by nature a disinfectant. It has the ability to eliminate physical harmful pathogens. Melaleuca, mentally and emotionally, also eliminates pathogens that lead to dis-ease. It is one of a few essential oils that interrupt old patterns of thinking. If you find yourself in a constant state of worry and anguish over the same issue, Melaleuca is a top oil to use.

Wintergreen and **Cypress** support Melaleuca. Wintergreen and Cypress have the equivalent energetic force of a jackhammer drilling through concrete. Together, all three are a force to be reckoned with, ensuring the pattern is broken. Whenever dealing with stubborn and stagnant energy, use these oils to break it up.

Lemongrass is the next best essential oil to clear low vibrational thoughts and emotions. It creates the desire to abandon complaining, cleanse negativity and welcome a fresh new outlook on life.

Cedarwood is used to calm the mind and balance out the formula. Melaleuca, Cypress, Wintergreen, and Lemongrass are fast moving and drying essential oils. The thick and rich properties of Cedarwood help to counterbalance the harshness of the clearing work of Melaleuca, Cypress, Wintergreen, and Lemongrass, and ensure transitions are gentle.

Additional Protocol

Apply Frankincense right after the application of the *Clear the Noise* blend to the bottoms of the feet. Rub one drop onto the bottom of each foot. Repeat this application twice a day, after the application of the blend, in the morning and in the late afternoon during days 1-7 of *Week 1*.

Frankincense Breakdown

Frankincense is an effective distributor of all other essential oils throughout the body and meridians. From a Chinese Medicine perspective, Frankincense affects the Heart, Liver, and Spleen. The heart is the main pump for moving blood, the Liver is the general of qi (the Liver is responsible for the smooth flow of qi throughout all organs/meridians), and the Spleen transforms the food we intake and turns it into blood to feed all the cells of our body. Frankincense takes care of the "nourish" and "harmonize" steps in the overall process of healing. Let's say that one of the noises you wrote down was, *I don't know what I'm doing.* After the clearing has begun, Frankincense helps to program the exact opposite. Therefore, you will experience feelings of *I know exactly what I'm doing and where I'm going.*

The body, mind, and spirit will need reinforcement to fully embody this new way of thinking and feeling. Hence, Frankincense harmonizes this truth all throughout your body. Other properties include moving blood and qi and relaxing muscles to improve blood circulation.

Diffuser Blend

USE DURING WEEK 1: DAYS 1-7

2 drops Lemongrass
2 drops Siberian Fir

Diffuse Lemongrass and Siberian Fir for eight hours during the day for a week. Diffuse this combination in a central area of your home. Best where you and your family spend the most time together. Our home is a sanctuary, and it is important to keep this space sacred. Diffusion will clear and restore the vibrations of the space, so even if you are not present during the day, you will still experience the benefits when you return.

Clear the Noise Diffuser Blend Breakdown

This powerful combination is the ultimate cleanser of repressed emotions and toxic thought patterns. They both have an effect on the lungs, which tend to store and hold regret, sadness, grief, contempt, bitterness, pride, and depression. These emotions are released when inhaling Lemongrass.

Lemongrass also brings awareness to what you need to let go of, and subsequently helps you embrace the next steps for your healing. The acrid flavor of lemongrass helps disperse buildup of negative emotions and moves lung qi.

Siberian Fir nourishes the lungs. It's an excellent pairing to support and counterbalance the intense movements from Lemongrass. Siberian Fir also regulates the smooth flow of lung qi. Most importantly, it begins with the process of forgiveness-- of others and self.

REVISIT WITH WRITING

At the end of the week of essential oil protocols, go back and revisit the five disempowering thoughts you listed. Rate each thought as you experience them today.

Next get a red pen and cross out everything you had written.

Below, write the exact opposite of the five you wrote previously.

1. _____

   _____

2. _____

   _____

3. _____

   _____

4. _____

   _____

5. _____

   _____

Whenever you need to release some noise, and it's natural to need a tune-up, you can revisit this protocol. It is a foundational and powerful protocol getting unstuck, especially when it feels like groundhog's day (again). You may not need to do a full week of this protocol in the future; it may be only one or two days. Trust your intuition. Listen to your body, thoughts, and emotions. They will tell you what needs attention.

I am so very proud of your progress and dedication!

Proceed to *Chapter 2: Replenish* only after you have finished all seven days of the *Clear the Noise* protocol. It is imperative that you allow your body and emotions the time needed to process the changes.

Chapter 2: Replenish

Replenish

I hope you are feeling significantly lighter after last week's protocols. Emotional de-cluttering is critical for health and well-being. Now that we have finished a decent layer of clearing, the next phase is a supportive one. Let's dive into the theory of yin-yang to help understand the overall healing process.

Yin-yang theory is one of the most important concepts to understand the nature of disease and proper treatment modalities. It represents the duality we see in nature.

Yin and yang are two stages of a cyclical movement, one constantly changing into the other, such as the day giving way to night and vice versa (Maciocia, 5).

YIN	YANG
Female	Male
Moon	Sun
Night	Day
Cold	Warm
Dark	Light
Inwards	Outwards
Contracting	Expanding
Passive	Active
Inside	Outside
Decreasing	Increasing
Below	Above
Slow	Fast
Damp	Dry

Yin and yang have opposing properties relative to each other. They are also interdependent and cannot exist without each other, just as day comes after night, and rest happens before activity. Nothing is completely yin or completely yang. In the yin-yang symbol, there is a seed of yin indicated by a black dot within the white area of yang, and there is a seed of yang expressed by a white dot within the black area of yin. When yin is weak, yang is in excess, and when yang is weak, yin is in excess.

"Extreme cold produces great heat, and extreme heat produces intense cold."
-from the classic text *HUANG DI NEI JING SU WEN*
(INNER CLASSICS OF THE YELLOW EMPEROR)

Yin transforms into yang, and yang transforms into yin. They transform into each other.

The focus of the last chapter *Clear the Noise* was around yang movement. There was significant activity and motion around the release of obstructions. In this chapter we move inward to replenish. Chapter 2: *Replenish*, focuses on yin activities that will add strength back into the body. (Throughout the book there will be work between yin and yang.)

Another important Chinese Medicine concept to discuss is kidney essence, or kidney jing. Our vitality and essence is stored in the kidneys, which determines longevity. As we age, our kidney essence becomes depleted. When we completely run out of kidney essence the human body dies. There are activities and ways of being that can either add to or take away our kidney essence.

What depletes kidney essence? Stress, fear, and insecurity are major contributing factors to disease and deterioration, along with excessive semen loss in men, women bearing too many children without recuperation and rebuilding after each birth, toxins in food and water, excessive alcohol and drug use, heavy metals, and excessive sugar (Pitchford, 360). Our thoughts and emotions are equally depleting to our health as a poor diet.

In the last chapter, *Clear the Noise,* we removed kidney-essence depleting frequencies.

In this chapter, *Replenish,* we will restore kidney essence and prepare you for the next chapter. When the auric field is cluttered with noise, a person will go into sympathetic mode, as the body interprets the clutter with danger and releases cortisol, thereby taxing the adrenals. We are not designed to continuously experience a state of emergency. All that noise in our field perpetuates this state of emergency and scatters qi (energy). Visualize vital qi leaking out of you drip by drip when experiencing continual anxiety, fear, and insecurity.

There is a time and place to experience fear, especially when it protects us from legitimate danger. All emotions are important and valid. However, there are appropriate seasons for every emotion. A continual state of panic is not appropriate. Our brains are so powerful that when we worry about a possible outcome our body experiences those emotions as though it were real. Most people live 70-80% of the time in these lower frequency states of fear, anger, anxiety, and danger mode. How liberating would it be to flip that percentage? What if 70-80% of the day we are filled with gratitude, and 20-30% of the day we are dancing with our fears? Higher frequency states lead to inspiration, creation and unconditional love.

Essential oils used in these strategic ways have the ability to change your state of emotions instantly so that you can progress throughout your daily life. Each step of progress compounds over time.

Progress is the goal, not perfection.

Even a 1% change day by day, week by week, will lead you to a vastly different destination. We must progress to feel fulfilled, even if doing so little by little.

Emotional exhaustion is a common daily struggle. In order to sustain life we must replenish our energy. The next protocol will help to conserve your vital energy and strengthen your spirit. Imagine pouring water into a cup that has holes on the bottom of the cup. No matter how much water you pour the cup will never fill up as the water leaks through those holes. The practice of replenishing as shown in this chapter will help to seal up the holes in the cup so that the cup can support and hold the flow of water.

Prior to removing frequencies of unworthiness, we must strengthen the body's qi. This strength of qi will enable the body to push unwanted vibrations of shame out with full gusto. If we clear too much, an imbalance of yang can arise and incur depletion, so we must balance the clearing activities in the last chapter with replenishing yin practices in this chapter to drive effective healing.

It is like training for a marathon. I remember the

training program that successfully got me through my first marathon. Throughout the months leading up to race day, runners are encouraged to follow a training program alternating days of long-distance runs with short-distance ones, and include some cross-training and rest days. This pace prevents fatigue, burnout and injury. A few weeks prior to race day, the recommended weekly mileage decreases. This period of slowing down allows the body to recuperate so that it has all the strength and energy to tackle the 26.2 miles with greater speed. If I had run 26.2 miles a few days prior to race day would I have had the strength to do so again the next day? Most likely not. This is the same principle when it comes to clearing low frequencies.

WEEK 2 PROTOCOL: Replenish

There are two parts to this week's protocol. This sequence applies to most people because many of us experience depletion at least one point in our lives. Signs of depletion include feelings of burnout and exhaustion. I have been there many times before-- you are not alone. To do intense work in a place of depletion can cause more harm.

This week's work of strengthening and replenishing will set the foundation for the next round of clearing we will be doing in the weeks to come. The next wave of clearing is fifty times more intense than the clearing in the first chapter. For that reason, this chapter will provide a buffer to decrease the intensity and length of recovery after those clearings. That is why it is essential to follow this protocol with care, particularly the sequencing and timing outlined here.

(You may use other essential oils topically, internally, or aromatically in addition to this week's protocol. However, the steps outlined here should be your baseline to start.)

Replenish

USE DURING WEEK 2: DAYS 1-7

TOOLS:

- ☐ 10mL Roller Bottle
- ☐ Fractionated Coconut Oil

ESSENTIAL OILS:

- ☐ Cedarwood
- ☐ Vetiver
- ☐ Coriander
- ☐ Eucalyptus
- ☐ Lemon
- ☐ Ginger
- ☐ Basil
- ☐ Juniper Berry
- ☐ Roman Chamomile

PREPARATION:

Add (5) drops of Cedarwood, (3) drops of Vetiver, (3) drops of Coriander, (2) drops of Eucalyptus, (3) drops of Lemon, (1) drop of Ginger, (1) drop of Basil, (2) drops of Juniper Berry, and (3) drops of Roman Chamomile into the 10mL roller bottle. Fill the rest of the roller bottle to the top with Fractionated Coconut Oil.

APPLICATION:

Roll the blend around the belly button (Ren 8) and two inches down to the lower abdomen (Ren 6). Apply two times per day: in the morning and in the late afternoon.

The Goal of the Replenish Blend

The goal is to affect acupuncture points Ren 8 (the umbilicus) and Ren 6 (approximately 1.5 inches below umbilicus). These areas stimulate original qi, which contains the kidney essence discussed early.

Ren 8 point translates as *Spirit Gateway*. This point is the umbilicus and is known as the entry and exit point of the spirit. Ren 8 strongly builds up original qi.

Ren 6 point translates as *The Sea of Qi*. It strengthens the kidneys, fosters original qi and regulates qi (DEADMAN, 505). Regulate qi means to create smooth, harmonious flow of energy.

Replenish Blend Breakdown

Cedarwood and **Vetiver** are the chief essential oils in this blend. Together they nourish yin and replenish essence to restore vitality. You will notice that these essential oils are thick and rich. Vetiver specifically replenishes kidney essence. Cedarwood opens the heart to receive love from others and the Divine. A closed heart doesn't allow for nourishment to take place. (Vetiver, when blended with these other oils, will not cause sleepiness.)

Coriander reminds us to prioritize our needs as well. For my generously, giving friends – please continue to do so. Don't ever change that. However, your needs must equally be valued so you can continue to give in a sustainable way.

Eucalyptus, **Lemon** and **Ginger** raise yang and help to circulate the thicker essential oils. Incorporating these oils helps to balance out the formula and enriches more yin and yang to build up your strength. These three oils provide mental clarity and will empower you to take responsibility for your wellness. I love using Ginger especially when I need to obliterate excuses for not doing what matters.

Basil and **Juniper Berry** are specifically designed for the exhausted soul. It strengthens the kidneys, increases qi, and provides a feeling of renewal.

Roman Chamomile harmonizes the blend. It provides a deep sense of peace, and a reminder that you have everything you need within you. All the talents, all the skills, all the love necessary for your wellness.

Diffuser Blend

USE DURING WEEK 2: DAYS 1-7

2 drops Frankincense
2 drops Lavender
2 drops Tangerine

Diffuse two drops each of Frankincense, Lavender and Tangerine during the day for eight hours in your bedroom. Your bedroom is a place of rest, restoration and sleep, which is a Yin activity.

Diffuser Blend Breakdown

According to Chinese Medicine, **Frankincense** has a dual function of nourishing yin as well as moving qi and blood. **Lavender** moves energy trapped in the lungs and heart and helps to open up the heart for receiving. Citrus essential oils, such as **Tangerine**, help to regulate qi, especially when using richer, nourishing essential oils. Tangerine prevents any stagnation from occuring.

There are periods when we function on auto-pilot and fail to reflect on what our daily motivations and behaviors are. As the focus of this week is on yin activities, the use of Frankincense and Lavender will move you into a state of reflection. These two oils will help uncover hidden parts of yourself that need voicing. You will discover at least one thing that must change to improve the quality of your life. This maybe something you have known for a while but have not implemented. However, this blend will create an intense desire to move forward. On another note, expect the unexpected. Surprises of movement may spring.

As Frankincense and Lavender incite reflection, Tangerine increases appreciation for the nourishment you are receiving. Many of us struggle with self-care, feeling a sense of guilt for putting our needs first. However, Tangerine helps us to find the joy in receiving, as much as the joy we experience in giving.

This blend/protocol can be used anytime you feel physically and emotionally burned out. Use it until you feel well rested.

A side note for my hypersensitive friends who are empaths and intuitive:

There is a percentage of people (around 5%), that do not do well with Lavender or Vetiver in the evening. Those are often used to promote and improve sleep. I have noticed that for hypersensitive individuals and empaths, Vetiver and Lavender will create more stimulation than relaxation. In case I get the question of *Can I diffuse this blend at night?* The answer is *yes* if these oils do not stimulate you. Again, listen to your body.

REVEALING THROUGH WRITING

As you move through this week with the oil application, write below what you have discovered that needs changing. It may be revealed on Day 1, 5, or 7. Whenever it does surface, commit to writing it down and implementing what you discover. No need for judgement. Just celebrate what you have been able to learn this past week. What a gift!

_____

_____

_____

_____

_____

_____

_____

_____

_____

_____

_____

_____

Replenish

_____

_____

_____

_____

_____

_____

_____

_____

_____

_____

_____

_____

_____

_____

_____

_____

_____

_____

Many Chinese Medicine concepts have been shared in this chapter, and I will continue to share more in the coming chapters. This medicine is over 5,000 years old with a rich history and a great deal of empirical data. It is one of the more complete, holistic, and comprehensive approaches to understanding human health and disease. My hope is to inspire an appreciation for the medicine as well as the lifestyle.

If you would like to learn more of the concepts and theories behind Chinese Medicine, here are a few of my favorite recommendations:

- THE WEB THAT HAS NO WEAVER by Ted Kaptchuk
- BETWEEN HEAVEN AND EARTH: A GUIDE TO CHINESE MEDICINE by Harriet Beinfield and Efrem Korngold

Proceed to *Chapter 3: Uncover the Shame* only after you have finished all seven days of the *Replenish* protocol. It is imperative that you allow your body and emotions the time needed to process the changes.

Chapter 3: Uncover the Shame

Uncover the Shame

As humans we will inevitably experience shame at one point or another in our lives. The phenomena of shame and worthlessness is a worldwide epidemic and a contributing factor of broken hearts and physical ailments. Researcher and storyteller Dr. Brene Brown, who has written many books regarding shame and vulnerability, explains how culture, family, social groups, media and communities perpetuate certain shame stories. This is a term she uses to describe the stories in our environment that get adopted unconsciously over time. Like a virus, shame stories often go undetected until it is too late. Luckily there is an antidote for shame.

Michelangelo worked day and night for two years carving the statue of David. Imagine your shame story as this 12,000-pound block of marble that must be carved to reveal the masterpiece that is YOU-- the glorious, stunning, magnificent, and breathtaking soul that is you. Instead of using Michelangelo's tools of hammer and chisel, your tools in this next chapter will be essential oils and writing. These tools will help chip away at the layers of shame and reveal the marvelous work of art you are. I can promise you that a one-time application of these protocols will not get rid of all the shame that we hold within ourselves and our human community. We must be patient and remain steadfast as Michelangelo.

CAN I TELL YOU MY SHAME STORY?

I would like to preface that I am usually hesitant to share my story. You may have observed that one of my stories has been, *People don't care about me or what I have to say.* This is a story I have worked on for the last few years and continue to do so everyday, and I am proud to say that I have made progress. In 2016, I published my first book I AM FABULOUS. I regularly create videos on social media and teach live workshops and courses around the world. Even though I still feel tinges of that story, I am no longer paralyzed with fear and have been sharing my healing art with those who are seeking it.

Much of my shame story stems from my relationship with my mother. She is a complex woman with a HUGE ability to love. She shares her love in the way that she knows best, and I have learned a great deal from her. The story I share here, I realize, is an interpretation, though, and I fully own and take accountability for the growth and healing process ahead for me.

Throughout my life, I never had to worry about physical security: I grew up in the suburbs of San Diego, California, attended private schools, pursued any and all extracurricular activities I desired and never had to ask twice about a new toy I wanted. Though my physical needs were more than fulfilled, what I craved most of all was attention from my mother. She worked

360 days a year, 15 hours a day, so there were many holidays, recitals, birthday celebrations, performances and so much more that she missed. To this day, even though she is approaching 70, she still keeps the same working hours! This dedication to her work resulted in many years of feeling disappointed and rejected as a child. It seemed as though making money was the most important thing in her life, not her daughter and family.

Here is a little background on my mother. My mother was born in Korea during the Korean War. From birth to age two, she and her parents struggled in war-torn conditions, constantly fleeing from danger. During the war, the North Korean army set their house on fire. As everyone was frantically escaping, my mother, an infant at the time, was left inside the burning house. A cow, however, ran into the burning house as it was trying to escape the flames in the adjacent barn. In efforts to save the cow, her grandmother ran after it and found my mother inside the burning house struggling to breathe. Had the cow and my great-grandmother not ran back into the house, who knows if my mother would be here today. My mother continued living in poverty until her teenage years. As a result, she vowed never to live in such poverty and hunger ever again. By the age of 23, she became a successful real estate investor in Seoul.

As an adult, I see how my mother's past haunts her and has left deep scars and trauma. Her very survival was at risk on a daily basis. Though I know her intentions were to make sure that I was provided for and had everything I needed, the little girl in me could not process her history and as a result I experienced abandonment and rejection instead.

I responded to feelings of rejection by working hard in school, hoping that my academic achievements would get my mother's attention. I would practice the piano until I had perfected each song, hoping a performance would get my mother's praise. But it seemed that the harder I worked, the less interested she became. Never once did I hear that she was proud of my A+ grades, nor did she comment or show any interest in the songs I would proudly play on the piano for her. After years of the same disinterested response, I came to the conclusion that, *People don't care about what I do,* and *I don't matter. I'm not good enough. I don't deserve love or intimate connection.* These feelings and beliefs shaped my choices as an adult, especially the types of friends and boyfriends I allowed into my world.

DIVING INTO WORTHLESSNESS

Not feeling worthy is essentially an expression of *I'm not enough. There is something wrong with me.* Or *I'm a bad person because.... I am a mistake. I am no good.* The dictionary definition of worthless is, "having no real value or use, a person having no good qualities, deserving contempt, of no importance; good for nothing."

Many of us struggle with feelings of worthlessness. Think back if you have ever told yourself:

I'm not good enough because I'm not at my ideal weight.

I'm a bad person because I smoke, drink, etc.
I don't deserve love because I am not perfect.
I'm not good enough because I am only making
$_____
I'm not good enough because I didn't graduate.
I'm a bad person because I eat sugar, processed
foods, ...
I'm not good enough because I don't own a house.
I'm a bad person because I'm not doing enough in
my business.
I'm not good enough because I can't get on top of
my to do-list.
I'm a bad person because I'm lazy.
I'm a bad person because I don't do _____

Do you constantly beat yourself up for not being a "better" parent, spouse, friend, partner, colleague, student, child of God? Do you experience on-going regret and self-disappointment in your heart? The voice of our inner critic can be blaringly loud, tearing us down moment-by-moment. It may have been a single moment in your past, a single criticism that you held onto, which became a part of your identity. That moment may not have involved words; it may have been someone's look. Whatever the trigger, this is why the work of clearing the noise in *Chapter 1* is key to start the process of healing. After we remove negative energetic influences of others' judgements, we can see more clearly what are the shame stories we have adopted as our truth.

Here are a few ways to uncover your shame story. Take a moment to do an inward inventory of the following questions:

• How often do you tell yourself *I should?* These *shoulds* incrementally chip away at our self-worth. For instance, *I should exercise more* can lead to *I'm a bad person because I don't take care of my body.*

• Do you obsess over perfectionism? The desire for perfectionism is a great disguise for shame because if we are perfect, then no one can criticize us. No one can shame us.

• What do you get angry about? Reacting defensively to criticism or feedback is a way of deflecting the shame we experience.

• What do you complain about or blame others for? When you blame another person in your life, what is the nature of the blame? Write out what exactly you are blaming that person for and dissect it. An example: I complain and blame my husband for not doing more around the house. When I break it down, it's because I feel I'm not doing enough around the house. That spirals into, *I'm not a great homemaker and mother, therefore, I'm worthless as a mother.* The fact that my husband is not doing more is irrelevant. The blaming is a projection of my own shame story.

• Where are you procrastinating? Is there a blog, podcast, website, conversation that you have been putting off? Procrastination is another form of avoiding potential rejection and judgment. If we never start that project, then no one can criticize us.

We choose to complain and blame for a reason. When we take a moment to dissect why we are blaming and complaining, we can see how these are certain topics we are struggling with internally. In those moments of high emotional charge, pay attention to where those reactions of anger, bitterness, disappointment, and sadness may be a reflection of shame in our own lives. When you get into "blame" mode towards loved ones, remember that blame is a reaction to our own shame.

WEEK 3 PROTOCOL: *Uncover the Shame*

This section covers three days worth of protocols for *Week 3. Chapter 4* covers the remaining four days of the week. As you work through the protocols, you will become painfully aware of your own shame as well as see others' stories. You will see how well you hid and deflected your shame story rather than embraced it. What I have learned about emotional healing is this: when we allow ourselves to experience the pain fully, then it can release. It's when we repeatedly avoid that the pain continues to fester. It's best to dive into your emotions to ultimately be free from them. Our western culture is constantly looking to avoid even the slightest discomfort.

Pain serves us, though, and provides important information. As the oils help you acknowledge and feel your shame, the next few days may be uncomfortable. Please be patient and gentle with yourself as you move through the pivotal moment of healing. The discomfort will pass. Just like a woman in labor experiences contractions, the pain may feel eternal and unbearable, but I promise it will pass.

NAME THAT SHAME

First it's your turn to write out your shame stories. You can use the five questions above to help you uncover your shame. Write out at least three shame stories. If you have difficulty, then you can revisit this writing exercise after the third day of this chapter's essential oil protocol.

_____

_____

_____

_____

_____

_____

_____

_____

_____

_____

_____

_____

Uncover the Shame

_____

_____

_____

_____

_____

_____

_____

_____

_____

_____

_____

_____

_____

_____

_____

_____

_____

_____

_____

I am Worthy

Uncover the Shame

_____

_____

_____

_____

_____

_____

_____

_____

_____

_____

_____

_____

_____

_____

_____

_____

_____

Uncover the Shame

USE DURING WEEK 3: DAYS 1-3

ESSENTIAL OILS:

☐ Lavender ☐ Wintergreen ☐ Black Pepper ☐ Frankincense

APPLICATION:

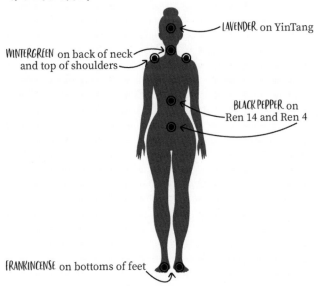

LAVENDER on YinTang

WINTERGREEN on back of neck and top of shoulders

BLACK PEPPER on Ren 14 and Ren 4

FRANKINCENSE on bottoms of feet

Apply the protocol in the morning before you start your day. You only need one drop on each of the areas listed.

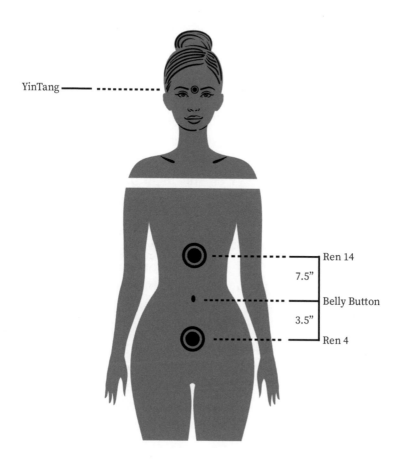

YinTang: centered in between the eyebrows
Ren 14: located 7.5" above the belly button
Ren 4: located 3.5" below the belly button

Uncover the Shame Protocol Breakdown

Lavender is the antidote to avoidance when applied on the YinTang acupuncture point. I recommend this application during the daytime rather than at night, as it may cause restless sleep. Lavender helps to curb distractions so that we can sit with the pain we desperately attempt to avoid. I'm guilty of this myself. My distractions or procrastinations of choice are watching documentaries and housework. When distractions get out of hand for me, I use Lavender. YinTang translates to *hall of impression*. It calms the Shen (spirit). In other cultures this is considered the *third eye*. Lavender on this location provides insight into the shame we are in denial of. If you have had trouble uncovering the shame in the writing exercise, then this protocol will help you see your truth.

Wintergreen is my all-time favorite oil for stubbornness. Often used to treat physical pain, Wintergreen can also be used to let go of emotional pain. It assists Lavender by aiding in surrendering to the pain that has been hidden. Much of our pain is stored within our body. Wintergreen on the back of neck and tops of shoulders opens up the gateway for our brain to register what emotional pain is being stored in our body. The opening allows the brain to consciously become aware of our subconscious patterns.

Black Pepper digs up all the surface excuses, revealing the underlying shame stories. Lavender creates the pause to help us pay attention to shame, while Black Pepper allows us to dive deep into the shame story. It is the oil that helps us fully experience that story, which subsequently assists in the release of the story.

The focus of this chapter's protocol is to rip out the

frequencies of shame. The accu-point locations are Ren 14 and Ren 4. Ren 14 is known as the *Great Gateway*. This point has a multitude of actions. It regulates the heart and unbinds the chest, calms the spirit, and regulates lung qi. Essentially, it relieves tension in the chest, where we hold many burdens in the heart and lungs. Regulating qi creates smooth and harmonious flow of energy within the organ and its respective meridian. Ren 4 is known as the *Gate of Origin*. It is a meeting point of the Spleen, Liver and Kidney channels (DEADMAN, 501). I prescribe this point to break up the shame from these organs and channels, as well as influence the sacral and root chakras. While Ren 14 addresses the upper body Ren 4 addresses the middle and lower body. Between the two points, they work to uncover shame hidden throughout the thoracic, abdominal and pelvic cavities.

Frankincense in this protocol serves to harmonize and support the healing actions of all the other oils.

Diffuser Blend

USE DURING WEEK 3: DAYS 1-3

3 drops Cardamom
1 drop Melaleuca
2 drops Eucalyptus

Diffuse the *Uncover the Shame Diffuser Blend* for eight hours in the main area of your home.

Uncover the Shame Diffuser Blend Breakdown

Cardamom diffuses anger and allows us to become an objective observer of the shame story. Not only will the protocol above help you to step into the shame, Cardamom also helps you to map out *when* and *how* the shame developed over the years. You will feel empowered by seeing the progression of your shame, rather than falling victim to it.

Melaleuca is the catalyzer to releasing the shame. This oil has the special ability to remove thought patterns that sabotage our healing efforts.

Eucalyptus strengthens the spirit and provides hope. When you apply eucalyptus, you will feel that there is light at the end of the tunnel.

Proceed to *Chapter 4: Pull the Roots* only after you have finished all three days of the *Uncover the Shame* protocol and diffuser blend. It is imperative that you allow your body and emotions the time needed to process the changes. After three days, you will be ready for the protocol in *Chapter 4: Pull the Roots* to continue "Week 3".

Chapter 4:
Pull the Roots

Pull the Roots

efore diving in, I want to congratulate you on coming this far. Everything we have done so far has been a preparation for this very chapter. You have named your shame stories, faced them head on, and experienced the depths of your pain. Now we are about to get down and dirty as we pull the roots of unworthiness out of our system.

Our spirit and body always know best how to heal themselves. As you use the oils, the most important shame stories will release over the next four days. Even if you were unable to identify all your shame stories in the previous chapter, your spirit will take care of the rest. Trust in yourself, and trust in the oils.

I highly recommend self-care supportive work throughout these next four days. Take epsom salt baths in the evening. Use one or two cups of epsom salt in a warm bath for a minimum of 15 minutes. Drink extra water and take walks to create circulation. Supportive essential oils will be included in this chapter to help you with this intense clearing. A great analogy for this session is a laboring woman who has finally reached the point of pushing the baby out. Ripping out your deepest feelings of unworthiness is a blessing. Your health, vitality, and joy for living shall all improve. Note that as we pull out the energy of unworthiness the essential oils will transform that energy from worthless to worthy.

Imagine how empowered you will feel when your internal monologue says:

I am worthy and deserving of love.
I am worthy of creating an impact in this life.
I am enough.

How differently would you show up in your relationships? Your spiritual walk? Your career? Most importantly, how much would you enjoy that internal peace and self-acceptance? When I truly began to love and accept myself unconditionally, knowing that I am cared for and deeply loved by my Creator, I fully understood that I don't have to do anything extra or need to earn this kind of love. It is just given. Though many of us have an intellectual understanding of these concepts, my goal is to move these concepts from the head to the heart and soul. Embrace your divine worth and beauty. From there, only miracles are created.

You, dear friend, deserve
♥ *Miracles* ♥

You deserve a supernatural life, above the complaining and moaning of what is wrong. It is the worthlessness that generates victim thinking. As you free yourself of low-frequency thoughts layer by layer, watch how everything changes. Even shifting 1% of the shame will lead to significant, positive outcomes.

WEEK 3 PROTOCOL: *Pull the Roots*

This section covers the final four days of *Week 3. Chapter 3* covered the first three days.

For maximum results, this protocol *requires* four days. If you miss a day, just keep going the following day.

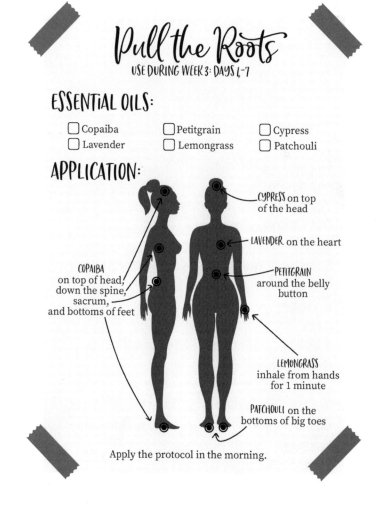

Pull the Roots
USE DURING WEEK 3: DAYS 4-7

ESSENTIAL OILS:

- ☐ Copaiba
- ☐ Lavender
- ☐ Petitgrain
- ☐ Lemongrass
- ☐ Cypress
- ☐ Patchouli

APPLICATION:

CYPRESS on top of the head

LAVENDER on the heart

COPAIBA on top of head, down the spine, sacrum, and bottoms of feet

PETITGRAIN around the belly button

LEMONGRASS inhale from hands for 1 minute

PATCHOULI on the bottoms of big toes

Apply the protocol in the morning.

Apply the protocol in the morning for the last four days of *Week 3*. For the Copaiba, do your best to reach as much of your spine. If you can, ask for assistance. You may use four to six drops of Copaiba, depending on your torso length. Apply a thin layer on the spine and sacrum. All other oils in this protocol only require one drop per application location.

Possible Side Effects

Immediately following the application of the protocol, you may have some side effects. Do not be alarmed. They are normal and fleeting. Effects may last up to 24 hours, however, they usually only last for a few minutes. (No side effect is fine, too.)

- Dizziness
- Shaky
- Flushed, redness in face
- Headache
- Tiredness (wanting to nap)
- Out of body experience (feel like you are watching yourself from outside)
- Emotional numbness (some transitions are experienced this way)
- Crying
- Rage
- Feelings of lightness and expansiveness
- Goosebumps
- Craving for physical exertion
- Anxiety, heart racing (usually five minutes)
- Resistance to completing the four days of this chapter
- Clearer vision
- Deeper Breathing/lots of sighing

If you experience more yang-type symptoms, such as feelings of anxiety and rage, wood essential oils are best for calming relief. In this instance, use Cedarwood or Grounding Blend on bottoms of feet and spine.

Pull the Roots Protocol Breakdown

Copaiba is the crème de la crème for clearing worthlessness. Shame is like a vine, entangling around all the organs and meridians. Copaiba has the ability to unravel the vines of unworthiness and pull the roots out entirely. Shame is literally being pulled out of you and transformed into worthiness. Copaiba is quite the sneaky essential oil, finding its way into every nook and cranny of your being to clear away hidden shame deep in your subconscious. Its effects are strong and require supportive oils to minimize the massive changes it spurs. We are applying this oil on top of the head, down the spine and bottoms of the feet to make sure Copaiba touches all organs, meridians, and chakras.

Petitgrain power, here we come. Petitgrain is like a bulldozer. It pairs nicely with Copaiba to give the push Copaiba needs to rip out the roots of unworthiness. Remember this oil when you desire to break self-sabotaging behaviors. The center of the umbilicus is an acupuncture point (Ren 8) called the *Spirit Gateway*. As the name indicates, this is where the spirit enters. This accupuncture point is a non-needled point. Instead, acupuncturists fill the belly button with salt, then burn moxa (mugwart) on top of the salt to warm up the area. (Consider the parallels of the umbilicus and the fetus: the umbilicus is how nutrients and sustenance are delivered to a growing fetus.) I have found that applying essential oils around the belly button is one location that quickly affects the entire body.

Cypress is for my hyper-critical friends. Do you have too many rules and standards to live up to? And when you don't fulfill those expectations, you conclude that you are a failure? Cypress is a secondary essential oil for clearing this kind of shame. It won't reduce your standards, as having high standards is excellent. What it will do is detach your sense of self-worth in relation to the outcomes of those expectations. The top of the head is where the internal channel of the Liver meridian ends. Cypress helps to release the pressure of the Liver through this point on the head. The Liver stores anger, frustration and resentment. Cypress allows us to embrace and release the frustration directed toward the self.

Lavender affects the Heart and Pericardium. A few of its TCM (Traditional Chinese Medicine) properties include expelling toxicity, clearing heat, and circulating qi. On the emotional level, Lavender is fantastic not only at surfacing repressed emotions, but also expelling them. Heat in the heart can translate to anxiety, agitation, anger, and irritability. Once the toxic, repressed emotions are released, Lavender smooths the flow of energy in the heart space.

Lemongrass is the clean-up crew. With all the activity of the other essential oils, a lot of dust gets kicked up. Any residue from all the clearing work will be taken care of by Lemongrass.

Patchouli helps you adjust to a new way of being. For many of us, our shame stories have become all too familiar. Eliminating them can be disorienting because those stories were what we used to make sense of our reality. This is why we must close the protocol with Patchouli. This oil reconnects us with our higher-self and familiarizes us to the world of worthiness. Patchouli is applied to bottoms of big toes to access the brain reflexology point, thereby helping the mind create new thought patterns of worthiness.

USE DURING WEEK 3: DAYS 1-7

2 drops Eucalyptus
1 drop Peppermint

2 drops Lemon
1 drop Lime

Pull the Roots Diffuser Blend Breakdown

Eucalyptus is the "everything is going to be ok" essential oil. Amidst all the change, you may need a friend to hug and comfort you. Eucalyptus is that friend-- an emotional doula. (I just gave birth to my third child, hence why I have been using a lot of pregnancy and childbirth analogies.)

Peppermint provides strength as you deep dive into the pain. It helps to make the process bearable and graceful. Peppermint opens up the airways. Combined with Eucalyptus, they cause you to breathe deeply through the pain.

Lemon provides mental clarity and a fresh perspective on your life's circumstances. It uplifts the spirit and instills hope for a brighter future. (EMOTIONS AND ESSENTIAL OILS, 61)

Lime empowers you to charge forward, no matter the difficulty, and conquer your shame stories.

Ways to measure if the protocol was effective:

- Less complaining about the usual things
- Increased gratitude and optimism
- Excitement and joy returning
- Bad habits lessening and addictions disappearing
- Desire and execution of healthy habits/activities
- End of procrastination on one or more projects
- Walking more confidently
- Taking bold risks
- Speaking up more and being assertive rather than passive

CELEBRATE BY WRITING

Celebrate the progress you have made in such a short period of time. Note the positive changes you have made after this protocol. The list above is not an exhaustive list, but a good place to start observing the new patterns you are creating.

_____

_____

_____

_____

_____

I am Worthy

Completing *Uncover the Shame* and *Pull the Roots* means you have completed the most challenging parts of this journey! The rest of the work is gentle and reinvigorating. Next is *Forgiveness,* then we will end with a profound and genuine sense of worthiness within you.

Proceed to *Chapter 5: Forgiveness* only after you have finished all fours days of the *Pull the Roots* protocol. It is imperative that you allow your body and emotions the time needed to process the changes. ♡

Chapter 5: Forgiveness

Forgiveness

I n the last chapter we focused on the yang activities of clearing unworthiness. This chapter focuses on nourishing the self with unconditional love and acceptance. Nourishment after clearing will help prevent self-sabotaging behavior that slips us back into old patterns. The work of forgiving in this chapter provides a fertile ground in which to plant seeds of worthiness, so be sure not to skip this step (or any step for that matter).

We may know the the value and importance of forgiveness intellectually, but how do we move the idea of forgiveness from the head to the heart? If you have been praying to experience forgiveness, I'm here to share with you how essential oils can assist you in this process.

Forgiveness is to love unconditionally. The work of forgiveness is one of the most important practices for improving spiritual development, emotional IQ, and professional success. This chapter specifically works on self-forgiveness. When we have compassion for ourselves it becomes easier to have compassion for others. Self-forgiveness is the beginning of unconditional self-acceptance and compassion. No longer do we need to operate from, *If I do ___, only then am I worthy of self-respect and love.* Instead, we can embrace ourselves with unconditional love, no matter our past.

Holding onto grudges and guilt gets old, literally. Did you know that one of the fastest ways to speed up the aging process is by holding onto grudges, guilt, and resentment? Re-telling stressful stories of the past robs you from experiencing what is good in the present and entangles you in a web of negative emotions that can weigh you down. Guilt, resentment, bitterness, rage, grudges, and judging are all contracted frequencies. Micro-expressions of these emotions manifest on the face and body and build up energetic congestion over time, causing wrinkles, hormonal imbalances and weight gain. The practice of forgiveness, however, can reverse these effects and help improve your physical, emotional, and spiritual condition. Forgiving does not mean we have to ignore the past, though. What if we took the valuable lessons in our past instead of dwelling on what went wrong? If guilt and grudges are metaphorically tightly closed fists, forgiveness then is the method of prying open those hands to receive healing and blessings.

Embracing forgiveness allows us to hear our true inner voice as well as divine inspiration. If you desire to live a supernatural life, where you experience miracles on a regular basis, then forgiveness work is a must. Many times the answers to our prayers and intentions are right in front of our face, but we cannot see or hear the answers because we are too consumed by the past.

In addition to forgiveness, we must take a personal inventory of our own shame stories. What grudges or resentments are you holding onto still? Holding onto these shame stories often leaks out onto others. Notice the next time you judge someone what emotions and thoughts come up for you. If there is a strong emotional charge in these judgments, take a moment to step back to see if you are projecting your own frustration of the situation onto them. When I experience intense emotions about another person, I use that opportunity to deep dive into my own shame story.

This type of personal accountability leads to freedom. We cannot control other people and their behaviors. We can only control how we respond to what comes our way. One side benefit of forgiveness work is that we up-level our electromagnetic signature-- the frequency we put out into the world. As a result, the type of people and circumstances you attract will also up-level. Dr. Joe Dispenza states in his book BECOMING SUPERNATURAL: "The only way we can change our lives is to change our energy – to change the electromagnetic field we are constantly broadcasting".

Unforgivingness binds and clots qi. We will be using essential oils that free the liver, strengthen the lungs, and open the heart. Anger constricts liver qi, and we need liver to function at its optimum levels because it is responsible for the harmonious flow of qi and blood throughout all the organs and meridians.

Sadness, grief, and regret affect heart and the lungs and deplete qi. Freeing up the lungs of stagnant energy allows you to breathe in new life. "The lungs are responsible for taking in new things. On a physical level this is simply the air that we breathe, but we need this function just as much on other levels - to take in new ideas for the mind and new life for the spirit. The word *inspiration* captures this wider sense on the lung's function." (WORSLEY, 47).

In the style of the Classical Five Element acupuncture practice, the heart has the title of *supreme controller*. The heart, like an emperor, creates order and delegates tasks to the rest of the other organs. When functioning optimally, the heart listens to the disputes and grievances of the other organs, and this wise ruler mediates without taking sides. The heart in return provides warmth, nourishment and unconditional love to all its subjects. "When the Heart is healthy everyone is filled with a sense of enthusiasm and joy, and their work becomes a source of pleasure. The goals and purposes which they all pursue are a source of fun, no matter how hard their tasks are. When the king is happy the whole of the kingdom cannot fail to be happy too (WORSLEY, 137)."

Addressing the liver, lungs, and heart is vital for effective forgiveness work. The roller bottle and diffuser blends in this chapter affect those three organs. You may cry tears of joy and relief as you apply the blends. You will quickly realize how heavy the burdens of guilt and resentment are after releasing them. Expect deeper belly breathing as you open up the space in your chest cavity. Those who have respiratory challenges may experience huge improvements as well.

Other benefits include increased gratitude, wishing others well, less irritability, more physical energy, and a desire to make significant changes. People will look more magnificent to you. YOU will look more magnificent to you. Look in the mirror intently and watch how much love you have for yourself. Rather than pointing out what's wrong in the mirror, you will highlight what is right. Another side effect I have noticed is the desire to remove clutter. Because forgiveness brings in a fresh, new perspective, a desire to let go of the "old" arises.

One last thing to mention, you may experience reconciliation with a strained relationship. It may come your way or you may be the one to initiate the reconciliation. Understand that embracing forgiveness does not necessarily mean you will receive an apology. We are doing internal work that is not contingent upon what others say or do. If it does come your way, embrace and receive that interaction.

WEEK 4 PROTOCOL: Forgiveness

Forgiveness
USE DURING WEEK 4: DAYS 1-7

TOOLS:

☐ 10mL Roller Bottle   ☐ Fractionated Coconut Oil

ESSENTIAL OILS:

☐ Ylang Ylang   ☐ Helichrysum   ☐ Bergamot
☐ Eucalyptus   ☐ Roman Chamomile   ☐ Lavender
☐ Cedarwood   ☐ Siberian Fir

PREPARATION:

Add (3) drops Ylang Ylang, (7) drops Helichrysum, (2) drops Bergamot, (4) drops Eucalyptus, (1) drop Roman Chamomile, (3) drops Lavender, (3) drops Cedarwood, and (5) drops Siberian Fir into the 10mL roller bottle. Fill the rest of the roller bottle to the top with Fractionated Coconut Oil.

PROTOCOL APPLICATION

Apply the roller bottle blend on Liver 14, inside both wrist creases, and around the belly button. Please note that there is a citrus oil in this blend, which may cause photosensitivity. If you plan to go out in the sun, apply the blend to the bottoms of the feet to avoid sun exposure.

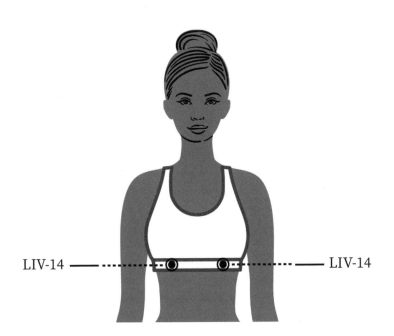

LIV-14 ⸺ ·········· ⊙ — ⊙ ·········· ⸺ LIV-14

Liver 14 is located down the nipple line, in the 6th intercostal space. For women, this is along the bra line. For men, this is directly below your pectoralis muscles, or where you might wear a heart rate monitor strap. This point is called the *Cycle Gate*. It is one of the more powerful points to free constrained liver qi. Applying the blend on this location relieves depression and self-directed frustration.

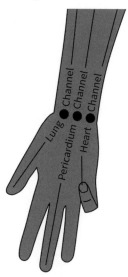

The wrist creases have three channels that pass through, including the heart, pericardium and lung channels. Oils applied on the wrist creases release the heart and lungs from sadness, grief, and resentment.

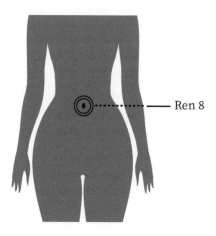

As mentioned in *Chapter 2*, Ren 8 is the acupuncture point around the belly button. Application of a blend on this location will enable fast circulation of oils.

Forgiveness Protocol Breakdown

Ylang Ylang prepares the heart to receive the forgiveness that Helichrysum brings. This oil opens the heart to receive love, nurturing, and healing. Ylang Ylang also helps release disappointment and betrayal.

Helichrysum is my favorite essential oil for forgiveness. On a physical level, this essential oil stops bleeding, clots open wounds, and alleviates pain. On a spiritual level, Helichrysum stitches up the open wounds of our heart so that no trace of scarring remains. As a result, we may freely recollect past events without the painful memories.

Bergamot cleanses self-condemnation. How many *shoulds* do you tell yourself in a day? I love how Tony Robbins states: *"Don't should all over yourself!"* Bergamot tackles self-criticism before it spirals into guilt and shame, and frees stagnant liver qi.

Eucalyptus in Chinese Medicine dispels external pathogens. It naturally expels that which does not belong. This essential oil pairs well with Bergamot to push out self-judgement.

Roman Chamomile helps regulate liver qi in a unique way. It is a soul-searching essential oil that helps recognize and acknowledge the desires of the heart while giving full permission to be authentic and to step into our divine path. Sometimes that path comes with great opposition, but not living our true path is infinitely more painful and frustrating. (EMOTIONS AND ESSENTIAL OILS, 84)

In the context of this blend, **Lavender** serves to keep us present with the feeling of forgiveness. It is easy to run away from the discomforts of forgiving, but Lavender will help you through this transition so you can move forward in your healing journey.

Cedarwood helps to balance out all the movement of the other essential oils in this blend, including Eucalyptus, Bergamot and Chamomile. When we have too many aromatic and moving essential oils, it can dry out yin. Remember that yin represents fluids and substance. Cedarwood also opens up the heart, thereby preventing loneliness and encourages receiving and seeking help from others.

Siberian Fir strengthens and regulates the smooth flow of qi in the lungs, allowing divine inspiration to enter. This oil also clears regret and sadness.

Diffuser Blend

USE DURING WEEK 4: DAYS 1-7

2 drops Eucalyptus
1 drop Cardamom
1 drop Helichrysum
1 drop Geranium

Diffuse the *Forgiveness Diffuser Blend* during the day for eight hours. As usual, it is not necessary to be in front of the diffuser the whole time. You can run the diffuser in the central part of your home while you are gone.

Forgiveness Diffuser Blend Breakdown

Eucalyptus reminds us that we are whole and complete. All the love and support we need is available to us at all times.

Cardamom is the oil for learning major life lessons. This oil assists in processing changes and paradigm shifts. Have you ever had your entire world turned upside down, changed your belief about something in a radical way, and found it to be earth-shatteringly difficult to go through? Cardamom makes the shift graceful. To move from unforgiveness to forgiveness is a radical change that requires the support of Cardamom.

Helichrysum is the oil that shifts your heart into forgiveness. **Geranium** is added to help you trust that you are safe, and that forgiving is a safe thing to do.

Once you have completed all five weeks of protocols in this book, you may use the *Forgiveness Roller Blend* and *Forgiveness Diffuser Blend* any time in the future. The blend can be used either before or after clearing stagnant energy.

WRITE FORGIVENESS

Alright my friend, you are in the final stretch! Close your eyes, take a deep breath and give yourself a mental hug for all the work you have done so far. Think of all the changes you have experienced throughout this week of *Forgiveness* and write them here.

I am Worthy

Proceed to *Chapter 6: I am Worthy* only after you have finished all seven days of the *Forgiveness* protocol. It is imperative that you allow your body and emotions the time needed to process the changes.♡

Chapter 6:

I am

Worthy

I am Worthy

Welcome to the grand finale my gorgeous friend! This is the moment you have been waiting for. It is now time to significantly increase your sense of self-worth, self-love and self-acceptance. You are worthy and deserving of all you desire. You are a magnificent being with infinite potential to create magic and miracles. If you have come this far in reading, I know you are not a person who settles and lives below your capabilities. You are a bold and courageous soul who fights for truth and charges against the status quo. A mundane existence is out of the question. You seek a supernatural existence. What others would claim impossible, you make possible. When we own our divine worth, we become a light to those around us. Be the example and give others permission to shine their beauty.

There are multiple benefits in owning your worth. I want to share with you the changes I have personally experienced as a result of worthiness. Prior to essential oils, I would easily be offended and hurt by others. This would create a strain in my relationships, as I held grudges and closed my heart from receiving love. One little criticism would send me to tears and take weeks of recovery. I played extremely small in life because I feared criticism and judgement. I also did not believe in myself as a healer and a leader and kept a small circle of friends and acquaintances. When I thought my voice did not matter, I kept quiet. I did not promote my work because I feared I was not good enough as a healer. It was a painful existence because I knew I had much to give, but I hid for many years in the shadow of my fears.

Once I fully accepted myself, the flame inside of me that I tried to keep small for so many years soon exploded into fireworks. I grew to respect myself and my work, and in turn others did too. Over the last several years, I have grown a large network marketing organization (in partnership with my dear husband), traveled around the world teaching workshops to thousands of faces, written a book on essential oils, re-started my healing practice, developed a 12-week course called AWAKE YOURSELF and had a third baby (while writing this book). Through it all, I am still madly in love with the man I married nearly ten years ago. Most importantly, my capacity for holding space for others has increased with my sense of self-worth. I used to be scared of holding too much responsibility and shied away from others. Now I feel like Superwoman.

Going through this five-week transformation does not mean all struggles and problems will disappear. Instead, you will develop an emotional maturity to gracefully address any and all challenges. The work of forgiveness and worthiness will strengthen your spiritual walk, whatever it may be. My communication and connection with God deepens as I receive the love given to me abundantly. As Albert Einstein said, "All that matters is the thoughts of God, the rest are details." Receiving love, especially God's love, is the beginning of healing. If you recall from the *Emotions and Frequencies* chart in the introduction, the frequency of love is very high, creating flow and expansion. Whether we are aiming for emotional or physical healing, love is required.

STAGNATION CREATES DISEASE.
Flow PREVENTS DISEASE.

Love creates massive energy flow.

Have you ever caught yourself being overly critical of others and being disgusted by this? I have. It is the nature of the ego to be critical. Developing your worth will decrease the amount of judging you do. When you can see the divinity in yourself, you can appreciate and see the divinity in others. Having this appreciation and respect for another changes your interaction with them. You may even develop an unlikely friendship.

Unworthiness pairs with fear. Low self-worth indicates that fear is likely preventing you from experiencing all the richness of life. When you feel unworthy, you are less likely to show up for life. You may be fearful of entering into a healthy relationship, applying for a job you desire, signing up for that yoga retreat in Costa Rica, promoting your work, moving to the city you've always wanted to live in, etc. Basically, any decision that requires faith, trust and courage gets put on hold because fear has won.

We humans are by nature creative beings. Any and

every work is creative--not just painting and poetry, but also leadership and science. When shame and fear are dominant, our creativity shuts down. We each have a unique perspective and contribution to the human community. Fear can beat down confidence and paralyze us into inaction. Writing this book, though, forced me to work on my shame story and overcome my fear of not being good enough. Understanding that I am worthy freed me to fully live my purpose and write this book. You, too, can live out the greatest expression of your soul and leave a legacy that makes you proud once you fully embrace that you are worthy.

When you do fully recognize how worthy and amazing you are you may notice the magic of manifestation. Energy flows smoothly, ideas come quickly, connections happen effortlessly, productivity skyrockets, passion ignites, and inspiration abounds. You feel alive. The groundhog-day kind of existence disappears. It is time for you to experience a life that is awe-inspiring. I cannot wait to see what comes to fruition for you.

I HAVE TO BE ME

My husband Alonto Mangandog and I wrote an affirmation poem called *I Have to Be Me*. I highly encourage you to read this aloud daily, once upon waking and once before going to bed. As you read it, fully feel the words sink into every fiber of your being. Remember, thoughts become actions, and actions become power.

I am Worthy

I Have to Be Me

I am worthy of love,
Just being me.
No need to do more.
I love who I see.

My worth is my own.
No one can take that from me.
If I want to be free,
I have to be Me.

I trust in myself
to know what is true.
Enjoy my life's journey,
and know what to do.

My voice is unique.
It needs to be heard.
The world shall feel
the power of my words.

I have all that I need.
Unconditionally loved.
Grace given to me
by my Father above.

My worth is my own.
No one can take that from me.
If I want to be free,
I have to be Me.

I am worthy of love.
Just being me.
All and all,
I am proud to be Me.

III

Let's get to work and receive all that worthiness.

WEEK 5 PROTOCOL: *I am Worthy*

I am Worthy
USE DURING WEEK 5: DAYS 1-7

TOOLS:

☐ 10mL Roller Bottle   ☐ Fractionated Coconut Oil

ESSENTIAL OILS:

☐ Indian Sandalwood ☐ Bergamot ☐ Myrrh
☐ Douglas Fir ☐ Grapefruit ☐ Wild Orange ☐ Cassia
☐ Rosemary ☐ Clary Sage ☐ Patchouli

PREPARATION:

Add (5) drops of Indian Sandalwood, (3) drops of Bergamot, (5) drops of Myrrh, (3) drops of Douglas Fir, (4) drops of Grapefruit, (2) drops of Wild Orange, (1) drop of Cassia, (1) drop of Rosemary, (1) drop of Clary Sage, and (1) drop of Patchouli into the 10mL roller bottle. Fill the rest of the roller bottle to the top with Fractionated Coconut Oil.

APPLICATION:

Apply the roller bottle blend on Kidney 3, the solar plexus, the spine, and the sacrum. Please note that there is a citrus oil in this blend, which may cause photosensitivity.

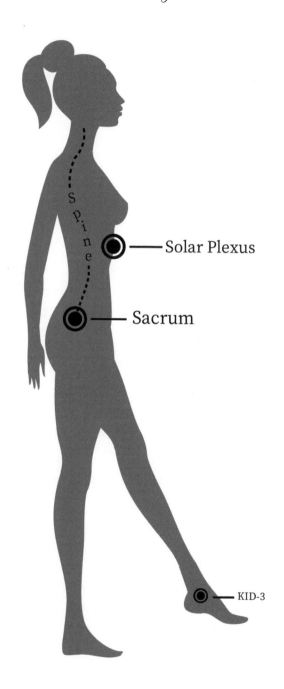

Solar Plexus

Sacrum

Spine

KID-3

Kidney 3 (KID-3) is located in the depression between the ankle bone and the Achilles tendon. Called the *Supreme Stream*, Kidney 3 nourishes kidney yin, tonifies kidney yang, and anchors the qi (DEADMAN, 340). The kidneys represent the core essence and nourishes all the other organs. When your kidneys are strong in worth, so too are the other organs. The rich wood oils in this blend nourish yin and are balanced by Cassia to increase yang.

The **solar plexus chakra** is located a few inches above the navel. It houses willpower, self-esteem and personal power. Application of the *I Am Worthy* blend here increases confidence and belief in yourself.

Application of the *I Am Worthy* blend along the **spine and on the sacrum** ensures that worthiness is distributed throughout the entire body so that every organ and meridian knows its importance.

I am Worthy Blend Breakdown

Indian Sandalwood and **Myrrh** are rich sacred wood oils that nourish yin and enrich the soul with divine worth. These oils take you out of fear and into heavenly realms, making you feel safe, important, taken care of, and grounded. Yin grounds yang and represents the blood and fluids in your body.

Bergamot, Grapefruit and Wild Orange essential oils increase self-acceptance, self-love and confidence. Citrus oils regulate qi in the solar plexus area and will help you assert yourself in the world. They also pair well with thick wood oils to help these more earthy oils circulate throughout the system.

Douglas Fir helps program new ways of thinking and being. Pair this oil with whatever new pattern you wish to establish. Douglas Fir also complements all the wood and citrus oils in the blend to solidify worthiness.

Cassia, though only one drop, is the linchpin of this blend. It fuels the wood and citrus oils to maximum effectiveness. This essential oil, known as the *oil of self-assurance*, will help you align with your mission and purpose (EMOTIONS AND ESSENTIAL OILS, 30). No longer will you shy away from your worth and capabilities. Just as a lion is meant to roar with ferocity, you too will claim your personal power fiercely with Cassia.

Rosemary is utilized when undergoing massive paradigm shifts. Your world view changes drastically from worthlessness to worthiness. This essential oil strengthens the mind and makes you resilient during dramatic transitions.

Clary Sage pairs well with Rosemary, as it provides wisdom and understanding to changes. Rather than reinforcing victimizing thoughts of *why is this happening to me*, or *I don't understand what's going on*, Clary Sage provides insight into your past, present and future.

Patchouli ties all the oils together and integrates them into the body. It works well with Douglas Fir to instill new patterns in the body and spirit. In addition, Patchouli brings about peace, stillness and an appreciation for the healing process.

Additional Protocol

Apply Neroli on your heart space, which is the sternum.

Neroli Breakdown

Neroli is the flower of the bitter orange. In Chinese herbology, flowers often used for the heart. Neroli, like a warm embrace, nourishes, strengthens, and opens the heart for self-acceptance. This oil is also beneficial for self-actualization work and for providing direction.

Diffuser Blend

USE DURING WEEK 5: DAYS 1-7
2 drops Douglas Fir
2 drops Eucalyptus
2 drops Lemon

Diffuse the *I am Worthy Diffuser Blend* for eight hours in a central part of your home.

I am Worthy DIffuser Blend Breakdown

The combination of **Douglas Fir**, **Eucalyptus** and **Lemon** is my *up-leveling blend*, used after significant clearing work has been accomplished. I also call this the *Self-sabotage Prevention Blend*. This trio sets new standards, creates lasting change, inspires healthy action, and provides mental clarity. It is a blend used to execute massive action towards your desired and destined path. You'll soon see that you're able to make great decisions quickly.

WRITE YOUR "A-HA" MOMENTS

Throughout the week, record your big "ah-ha" moments and notable changes that have taken place. Check in with your feelings and thoughts, and see if there has been a change in your internal monologue. Pay attention to the interactions you are having with your family and friends. Is anything different? Are you receiving more good news? What are your "wins?" How is your physical energy level? Have your taste buds changed? Record anything and everything worth mentioning.

_____

_____

_____

_____

_____

_____

I am Worthy

I am Worthy

You did it! You completed the five-week transformation to worthiness! I am so proud of your dedication and bravery. Welcome to this new-found emotional freedom, personal power, and unlimited creativity available to you. You have tools from this book to carry you through hard times and transitions. Just as we must continually eat wholesome foods and exercise to maintain our physical well-being, we must also use tools regularly to improve our mental, emotional, and spiritual well-being. There are many ways to create healing, and I hope that you have found a new empowering set of tools with essential oils.

Feel free to re-visit this five-week process whenever you feel stuck or need a tune-up. Listen to your intuition. This might be once a year or every three months. I suggest documenting the process every time you go through it. As humans, we tend to forget all the magnificent things that are happening and focus on what is wrong. Start to frame your mind to see what is working and acknowledge it as you go every time you write. Let your writing be a moment to praise and celebrate.

Before we say goodbye, I have a few more things to share in our final chapter.

Conclusion

My dear soul friend,

It has been an absolute honor guiding you through this emotional work. I have found that once you understand that your worth is infinite and you fully own it, you become unstoppable! It is your time to make a beautiful mark in this world, leave a legacy and share your art with all of us. When you step into this space of living your art, it creates a feedback loop of expanding worth. The world needs you to show up fully.

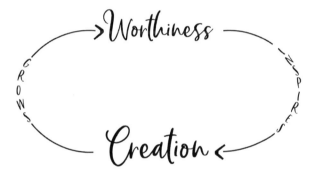

As you move through multiple cycles of growing your worthiness and inspired creation, they expand simultaneously. You move from believing you are worthy to *knowing* you are worthy.

Owning your worth leads to the removal of noise and flowing inspiration. This allows you to hear the music of life and to create your unique art. As you share your art, the human community benefits and the world expands. As the world expands, so too does your worth. It's a beautiful cycle of growth.

This book was created specifically for you so that you could close the gap between "potential" and actualization. I know firsthand how playing small can kill the spirit. Worthlessness is a barrier to greatness. Thankfully we have tools like essential oils to remove these barriers.

I love you dearly my soul friend. I hope to see you in person and give you a big hug. Remember, you are worth it. Run after your dreams and shake up the humdrum life. And trust that all the people, tools, resources you need to make things happen always show up at the perfect time.

I would love to hear from you and your journey. Please contact me...

Thank you again for sharing your energy and making the world a better place.

You are Worthy,

Desiree

The biggest adventure you can take is to ♥ live the life of your dreams.

-Oprah Winfrey

CONTINUE WORKING TOGETHER

Our time does not have to end here. If you would like to continue working with me, visit my website *www.desireemangandog.com*. There you will find ways to dive deeper in your journey. Here are a few starters:

- I AM FABULOUS BOOK: Improve your emotional well-being with 45 essential oil recipes

- AWAKE YOURSELF COURSE: Shed limiting beliefs in your conscious and subconscious mind that are preventing you from greatness. This course is a MUST to create lasting changes for your spiritual, emotional and mental growth.

- Private Sessions: Get customized essential oil protocols, based on your needs in a Private Session with me. I can identify your root causes of imbalance and walk you through a protocol during the session, as well as customize a program to last you three months.

- Live Events: Hear me speak at a live event or webinar. For upcoming events check out www.desireemangandog.com/events

You can also find a me on Facebook, Instagram, and Youtube, where I post free content.

Facebook:

www.facebook.com/DesireeFabulousMangandog/

Instagram: @DesireeMangandog

Youtube: www.youtube.com/desireemangandog

Resources

Should you feel inspired to learn more about the concepts discussed in this book, here are some of my favorite resources to get you going.

Practice You by Elena Brower

Lucky Bitch by Denise Duffield-Thomas

Breaking the Habit of Being Yourself by Dr. Joe Dispenza

Between Heaven and Earth: A Guide to Chinese Medicine by Harriet Beinfield

Bibliography

Deadman, Mazin Al-Khafaji, & Baker. A Manual of Acupuncture. East Sussex, England: Journal of Chinese Medicine Publications, 1998.

Enlighten. Emotions and Essential Oils. Salt Lake City: Enlighten Alternative Healing, LLC, 2017.

Maciocia, Giovanni. The Foundations of Chinese Medicine. Oxford: Elsevier Churchill Livingstone, 2005.

Pitchford, Paul. Healing with Whole Foods. Berkeley: North Atlantic Books, 1993.

Worsley, J.R.. The Five Elements and the Officials. Taos: Redwing Book Company, 2000.

REPLENISH BLEND by Desiree Mangandog
INGREDIENTS: Fractionated Coconut Oil, Cedarwood, Vetiver, Coriander, Eucalyptus, Lemon, Ginger, Basil, Juniper Berry, and Roman Chamomile
APPLICATION: Apply the roller blend on REN-8 (around the belly button) and REN-6 (two inches down to the lower abdomen).
CAUTION: Citrus oils may cause photosensitivity.

♥Replenish

FORGIVENESS BLEND by Desiree Mangandog
INGREDIENTS: Fractionated Coconut Oil, Ylang Ylang, Helichrysum, Bergamot, Eucalyptus, Roman Chamomile, Lavender, Cedarwood, and Siberian Fir
APPLICATION: Apply the roller blend on LIV-14, the wrist creases, and on REN-8 (around the belly button).
CAUTION: Citrus oils may cause photosensitivity.

Forgiveness

I AM WORTHY BLEND by Desiree Mangandog
INGREDIENTS: Indian Sandalwood, Bergamot, Myrrh, Douglas Fir, Grapefruit, Wild Orange, Cassia, Rosemary, Clary Sage, and Patchouli
APPLICATION: Apply the roller blend on KID-3, the solar plexus, the spine, and the sacrum.
CAUTION: Citrus oils may cause photosensitivity.

♥I am Worthy♥